ADVANCE

John Henry Fleming's *Fearsome Creatures of Florida*
is required reading for anyone who lives in Florida, has
ever lived there, has relatives who live in Florida, ever
went to Florida on vacation, has ever flown over
Florida on route to somewhere else, has ever dreamed
about Florida, ever even once had a fleeting thought
about Florida, ever heard Delius's *Florida Suite*, or ever
read Charles Willeford or John D. MacDonald. Much
ingenuity, much wit, much verbal magic — this book is
sheer pleasure.

—Peter Straub, author of *In the Night Room*
and *Ghost Story*

FEARSOME CREATURES
OF FLORIDA

John Henry Fleming
Illustrations by David Hazouri

To Mrs. VanDeBoe,
Thanks for being such a
fearsomely wonderful teacher!

Pocol Press
Clifton, VA

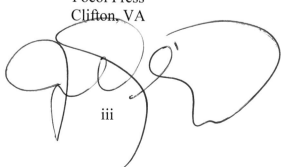

iii

POCOL PRESS

Published in the United States of America
by Pocol Press
6023 Pocol Drive
Clifton VA 20124
www.pocolpress.com

Publisher's Cataloguing-in-Publication

Fleming, John Henry.

Fearsome creatures of Florida / John Henry Fleming ;
illustrations by David Hazouri. -- 1st ed. -- Clifton, VA :
Pocol Press, c2009.

p.; cm.

ISBN: 978-1-929763-40-5

1. Animals, mythical--Florida. 2. Monsters--
Florida. 3. Animals--Florida--Folklore I.
Hazouri, David. II. Title

GR825 .F54 2009
398.24/54759   0904

ACKNOWLEDGMENTS

Thanks to my wife, Julie, and my kids, Hayley and Ethan, for their support and encouragement. Thanks also to the University of South Florida for the time and resources to research and write this book. I am indebted to many helpful websites for credible information, unconfirmed rumor, and the fertile wilderness between, including Wikipedia, The Cryptozoologist, Cryptozoology.com, The Cryptid Zoo, The Florida Skunk Ape website, The Florida Panther Society website, Florida Panther Net, Weeki Wachee Springs website, The Mystery of the Wakulla Volcano, and the Florida Department of Environmental Protection website. Finally, I owe acknowledgment to William T. Cox's 1910 book, *Fearsome Creatures of the Lumberwoods*, for providing the original spark to write this one.

A portion of the royalties from the sale of this book will be donated to nonprofit environmental preservation groups in Florida.

Disclaimer: Any resemblance of these creatures to the one now standing behind you is purely coincidental.

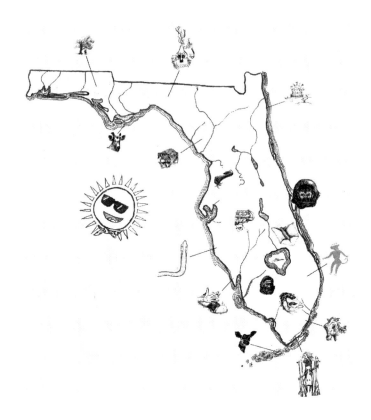

Fearsome Creatures Habitat

TABLE OF CONTENTS

TABLE OF ILLUSTRATIONS

INTRODUCTION

Driving an isolated highway at dusk, you detect an enormous shadow passing between trees, a looming man-monster with Flo-Jo claws and Nosferatu schnaz. By the time you look, if you even bother to, it's gone.

You shake your head. It was nothing. A trick of the light. A projection of idle thoughts.

Mowing your grass, you feel a pair of hands reach up and grasp your ankles. A flash of thick gray knuckles, then another. Was it a crimp gang trying to shanghai you into the underworld? Impossible. Probably just a sprung vine of unmowed St. Augustine grass snagging at your socks.

You back up and re-mow, dutifully following the mower as it blazes its well-worn trail like a printer reprinting—same words, same page, week after week.

We've grown accustomed to denying what we see with our own eyes. In our cars, we turn up the radio to distract us from shadows. We travel between the lines on a flat ribbon of pavement, our disbelief so habitual denial is our first inclination. Even "denial"—with its suggestion of conscious effort—doesn't accurately describe what we do. It's a reflex, an automated sensory gate that locks out the unpleasant, the uncomfortable, the strange. Behind the gate, safe within, we drift through a life that is safer, more comfortable—and pale.

It's that promise of comfort and ease that draws so many to the state of Florida. They flock here by the millions—for vacations, for easy living, for retirement. Their eyes see only sunsets and swimsuits. Their ears hear only cartoon mice and tiki-bar Buffetteers. Their noses smell only coconut sunblock and the freshly-quaffed Bermuda grass of our finest golf courses.

From Ponce de Leon to Walt Disney, pleasure-seekers have washed up on Florida shores and declared the land a blank canvas on which to paint their visions of earthly paradise. But an earthly paradise requires a fence, a way to keep out what's ugly, dangerous, or otherwise unacceptable. Even the Garden of Eden had its boundaries. Today, there are walled and gated developments in Florida by the thousands, little Edens with vigilant, uniformed guards charged with improving upon the gatekeeper of Eden, who, after all, couldn't keep out the snakes.

In exchange for inflated real estate prices and monthly dues, these developments promise their residents a bounded, exclusive, usually golf-themed paradise. Unfortunately, the communities aren't entirely self-contained, so residents are sometimes compelled to travel outside the walls to work or shop, averting their gazes from monsters of any kind—not only serpents in the grass but gators with watchful, 50-million year old eyes, as well as your everyday human riff-raff, your one-armed vets God-blessing America and begging for dollars at intersections, your vacant-eyed streetwalkers hustling for drugs, and your rival gangs firing into each other's mother's front windows—all the lowly unfortunates who can't afford a home on the links.

Looking away is a finely honed skill, one that rewards with a flat-line existence of impenetrable satisfaction.

But shouldn't there be more?

This book's modest goal is to make at least some readers—those not settled too comfortably into the lanai of their prefab paradise—turn their heads to the man-monster's shadow next time, to suppress for a moment the instinct to deny. Entertain instead the possibility that what you see may be real after all. And if you're still not sure, allow yourself to rest uneasily for a time, to live in a state of charmed uncertainty rather than in a picture postcard or a development brochure.

There are rewards to it. You'll be making the world richer rather than just yourself.

—JHF

The Glades Python

It made the national news: 13-foot Burmese python tries to eat 6-foot alligator, explodes. Pictures at eleven. A huge, belly-up python split like a roll-paper tube when an undead gator kicked its way out.

Other than a change in the mosaic pattern—the python's belly like a dot-matrix print-out, the gator's a primitive set of rectangular tiles—the one looks like a natural extension of the other.

It's a coiled mystery, a reptilian time machine. A glimpse—surprising to some—of the Darwinian struggles alive and well in the Florida glades.

How could it happen here, today, just beyond the condos and golf courses and practically in our own back yards?

I'll tell you.

It begins like this: A boy craves a pet and dreams big. No garter snake for him. Nor a boa, since half his fifth grade class already owns one. No, if he really wants to earn his classmates' respect, he must have a snake that can grow to 20 feet, one that can suck down pet Easter bunnies as quick as a trip to the flea market.

A Burmese python fits the bill.

His parents indulge him. They answer a classified and bring him a fork-tongued pal named Phineas, who stares through the glass like someone just stole his food.

For a time, the boy basks in the notoriety of his storybook pet. New friends line up out the door to watch the Saturday afternoon feedings, when a live rat tunnels head-first to its death. But when the snake reaches eight feet, the boy's parents begin to wonder if they shouldn't have just bought him a shrunken head— a thing just as frightening but with the advantage of being dead. This snake is alive, and it's growing.

How easily now it could strangle the boy's younger sister.

And soon, the boy himself. Already, the boy has felt his ribs creak like old wood when Phineas squeezes him playfully around the middle, and his karate lessons offer no defense. The snake has graduated from merely exotic, a label that implies a strange thing tamed, a caged bit of otherness. Now the aura of danger has become danger itself.

When the thing measures ten feet, Dad and two friends load the cage into the bed of a pickup and drive it into the Everglades, where it would seem to pose no threat to anyone, or to anyone's dogs and cats.

But in the wet, rich glades, the thing thrives. It is no longer a dangerous pet and no longer an exotic stranger. It is right at home.

It feasts on otters, rats, turtles, and endangered wood storks. It finds others of its kind—former pets—and it breeds. Slithering quickly up the food chain, it soon comes face to face with the American Alligator.

Who will swallow whom?

When both reach a certain size, it's a simple matter of surprise and strategy. As the pictures showed, even an apparent victory can end in mutual defeat. Yet the python nearly succeeded.

And there are plenty more, adapting so well you have to wonder if this is where they belonged all these millions of years, a kind of ophidian Promised Land.

Bruce Lee said, "When two fighters of equal strength, speed, and skill are matched, he who is master of the feint will win." Who can doubt that the python, the adaptable newcomer, will be first to master the feint.

And once the alligators have been suffocated and swallowed whole, where will the 20-foot python go to satisfy its insatiable hunger for big, slow-moving sun-worshippers?

It will follow the line of pick-ups back from the Everglades. It will sinuate through the ficus hedges between neat rows of backyard pools.

And there, with the patience of a creature whose evolutionary rewards come once every million years, it will wait.

The Glades Python

The Skunk Ape

Every culture has its hairy doppelganger, its slinking, upright cryptid to haunt us with evolutionary might-have-beens. We glimpse them deep in the shrinking nowheres, moving away, turning at the last moment with a knowing look: If the climate had been different, or the prey less scarce, or if the earth had wobbled the other direction, I might have been you. Their names we know from legend: the American Bigfoot, the Canadian Sasquatch, the Tibetan Yeti, the Australian Yowie, the Brazilian Mapinguary, the Wild Man of China, the African Chemosit. Some we know by grainy video, others by secondhand anonymous reports, still others by plaster casts of their enormous feet.

Only one do we know mainly by smell.

Spotted most frequently in and around the Big Cypress Preserve, a 700,000-acre hideaway thick with cypress, pines, and tall-grass prairies, the Florida Skunk Ape is variously described as an eight-foot orangutan, a beleaguered escapee from Monkey Jungle, and a man-faced black bear. Still, sightings are rare; more often, sportsmen and wanderers detect its overpowering stench.

"Like a dog that ain't been bathed in a year and suddenly gets rained on" is how one witness describes the smell. Others, less generous, claim it's more like the uncleaned cage of an elephant with intestinal trouble, or the county dump after a methane explosion has scattered its ripe innards, or a bubbling witches' vat of garlic, excrement, and putrefying fish. It's an experience you don't forget.

Who can explain it? Does it feed its glands with a diet of skunks and turkey vultures and the rotting flesh of abandoned prey, gathering their foul odors with the panache of a French saucier? Or does it roll in the refuse of humans and the offal of butchered beasts, matting its fur in fetid precision like an artist mixing paint? A stench like that suggests a conflicted view of its own celebrity; it wants to be known, and also to be left alone. As it paces through field and forest wrapped in the protective cocoon of its own reek, it also wafts its celebrity to anyone in a three mile radius. Think how many artists in history have found merit in just such a stance toward the viewing public. Their bristly arrogance shuts out the world, while their art brings them renown.

To be famous and left alone: it is the ideal condition for a working artist. Except the Skunk Ape gathers the seemingly conflicting motives into a single act: the art of bad publicity.

Appreciate the Skunk Ape on his own terms, as you would any artist. When you are driving a lonely stretch of the Tamiami Trail late at night and find yourself stranded with a pair of blown-out tires and your cell phone out of range, roll down your window and breathe in the reek that churns your stomach and floods your mouth.

Be brave, and lose your preconceptions. Close your eyes. Flare your nostrils. Let your nose sift through the bold, ripe collection of nauseating tones that will soon make your guts convulse.

Then, as you vomit on the shoulder, alone in the dark with your thoughts, you can appreciate the technique of the Skunk Ape, the infamous artist of stink.

The Skunk Ape

The Mangrove Man

Like its namesake, the Mangrove Man thrives in coastal environments, rests on a set of woody spider legs, and filters salt to receive liquid nourishment.

One key difference: while the mangrove filters salt from brackish coastal water, the Mangrove Man filters it from the blood of its victims.

The Mangrove Man camouflages itself in the twilight interiors of estuarine mangrove stands, where even an idling boater would be hard-pressed to spy its angled, sad-looking eyeballs or the crab-like twitches of its spindly legs.

A boater who anchors and wades ashore may mistake the creak and shush of the monster's movements for the sounds of the usual creatures that call the mangroves home—snook, crabs, spoonbills, ibises, turtles, and rats, among others.

As the boater rests on the secluded beach in solitary contemplation, he may not notice the raised leg of the monster with its stake-like tip that easily pierces flesh and sucks it dry.

And yet the boater is safe because the Mangrove Man is content to rest in the shadows.

It wants simply to be left alone.

If the monster were capable of empathy, it might have some communal feelings for the contemplative boater. There they rest, nearly side by side, a man with his thoughts, a monster with a desire for solitude that outweighs all else, even the need for food. And there they'll remain, until either the boater's quiet mood has passed—at which point he wades back to his boat, pulls anchor, and motors away—or the boater hears a snap in the mangroves, his curiosity gets the better of him, and he shoves his way through the dense tangle of prop-roots and the driftwood, beer cans, and rotting seaweed, only to come face to face with a set of raised wooden spikes and infuriated orbs.

If its habitat went undisturbed for as little as a year, the Mangrove Man would still not emerge to feed, and would surely grow extinct. Its *raison d'être* is to hide itself away. There are people who moved to Florida for the same purpose and find themselves more and more disturbed. Perhaps they can sympathize.

Who knows what the Mangrove Man thinks as it crouches among the mangroves? Does it even matter?

At first glance, the Mangrove Man might seem an ideal poster child for our threatened coastal environment. But think what the poster might look like: A hideous, sad-eyed monster framed by mangroves, its tear-streaked face pleading, "Please let me starve in peace."

Smoke pours from an environmentalist's grain-fed ears. Spontaneous combustion follows.

It's a prickly environmental paradox seen nowhere else on earth: preserving its habitat means threatening the monster with extinction; preserving the monster means allowing developers—and curious boaters—to encroach on its dwindling habitat.

And yet the environmentalists can take heart in the monster's confrontations with developers. A few years ago, one beautiful old stand of red mangroves along the Indian River was wiped out by an "accidental" fuel spill. The spill just happened to occur on the banks of a property recently acquired by the Redoubtable Development Corporation. With the mangroves gone, the RDC was free to develop the land without government interference.

But when RDC board members toured the property late one afternoon, they were surprised to find one small patch of mangroves still standing.

The board members followed the remnants of a two-track pioneer trail down to the waterfront and parked their golf carts beside the sickly but still living mangrove clump. Wavelets lapped at the knots of decaying roots, and a pair of egrets stepped over the eyeless carcasses of rotting fish.

The board members held their noses and wanted badly to escape to fresh air, but they also knew they'd have to get rid of these last few mangroves before someone from the Department of Environmental Protection took notice.

Fortunately, they'd come prepared for just this possibility. One of them opened his cart's built-in cooler and pulled out a can of gasoline to sprinkle on the roots.

"Shh!" is all he said, finger to lips, smiling. He crept into the mangroves, crouched, his eighty dollar tie tucked into his shirt, while the others folded their arms or put their hands in their pockets and watched.

Three steps in, he stopped and twisted like he'd heard a noise.

Nothing.

He unscrewed the gas cap and reached through a spindly set of branches to pour gas over the roots.

That's when the thing jumped to life.

The one survivor later remembered a pair of egg-shaped glaring orbs. And then, before anyone understood what was happening, the mangrove's branches came alive and pierced the flesh of the board member with the gas can.

Swiftly pinned to the sandy bank, the man was sucked dry as the gleaming orbs filled with blood. Two other board members tried to help and were in turn pierced and drained. Another was impaled as he tried to run.

The survivor has refused to speak of this event—or to go near a mangrove—ever since. RDC dissolved, and the property sits to this day undeveloped.

Today, a solitary clump of mangroves rests on the banks as if in quiet contemplation of its fate.

Or someone's.

The Mangrove Man

Creatures of the Groves

A citrus worker balancing high on a ladder and stretching for ruby red grapefruit is a sensitive instrument for detecting the rumbles and thuds of approaching beasts. And the view from the top allows workers to see, deep in the groves, what others might miss: the Halloween striping of a Bengal tiger's back leg as it lunges between rows, the drooling, black-stained jaws of a busy clan of hyenas, the implacable yellow eyes of a black jaguar staring with unearthly stillness.

None of these sightings is all too surprising in a state where there's a long history of exotic animals set free from defunct tourist traps and amateur zookeeps with cages in back of their lonely singlewides. And yet there are other, still fiercer creatures whose names and descriptions get shape-shifted as they're passed around at migrant camps and translated from one native language to the next: from Zapotecan to Mam, from Mixtec to Kanjobal to Tzotzil.

Here are the crude English translations of a few:

The **Globesucker** is a ferret-like creature with an elongated body, wide jaws, and sharp teeth. The flying-squirrel skinflaps between its front and rear legs allow it to leap from tree to tree, where it sinks its finger-sized fangs into grapefruits and oranges. Because it feeds in the colorless light of dusk, it pounces on anything globe-shaped, quickly piercing the flesh to suck out its juices. The globesucker is one good reason citrus workers do not allow their children into the groves after hours.

Cage Spiders work quickly in teams to trap their prey in citrus trees. A worker stretching too far into a tree to fill his pick-sack may get his small prize but find himself trapped in the twilight of a webbed dome, a thousand tiny spiders having communicated by mysterious means and gone to work in an instant. The web is not so strong that a grown man can't escape, but we all know how twitches and spasms get a spider's attention; by the time a man gets his fingers through the web, it's too late for the rest of him.

Reports of **Shaker Gremlins** have become more numerous in recent years, owing to citrus companies' increased use of canopy shakers. Canopy shakers look like the rotating brushes in an automated car wash, except the brush is vertical and the bristles are metal poles that knock fruit off the trees as they rotate, eliminating the need for even the cheap, undocumented labor of human fruit pickers. The shakers work in pairs, churning slowly through the rows on either side of the trees. Pickers fear the mechanical canopy shaker, and not just because it can put them out of work. Shaker gremlins can get hold of the mechanical shakers, even in broad daylight, and by the time workers realize there is no operator—at least no *human* one—the whirling tines descend like the clubs of a thousand merciless field bosses.

It's not simply the hard work that makes life for grove workers dangerous and short. If state lawmakers were as honest as they are vainglorious, they'd require the oranges on Florida license plates to drip with sweat and blood.

The Globesucker

Storm Devils

Storms are trouble in Florida, and not simply because the state sticks its neck into the path of the spinning one-eyed monsters we call hurricanes. Other states get those, but only Florida has Storm Devils.

In the calm between storms, Storm Devils are indistinguishable from other animals you'd find in the suburbs—squirrels, rabbits, skunks, possums, raccoons, black racers, crows, red-cockaded woodpeckers, stray cats. For all intents and purposes, Storm Devils *are* these animals while it's calm. They slink across your lawn at dusk. They hide in your bushes. They perch in your trees.

Only when a storm hits do they reveal their true nature.

When the rain starts to fall, most creatures seek shelter in burrows or nests, shrubs or trees. Not the Storm Devils. The lightning flips an internal switch and draws them out as Dr. Jekyll's potion draws out Mr. Hyde. When the thunder quakes across their feathers, fur, or scales, they tremble as if coming to life for the first time. They soak up the downpour like a dry sponge, growing in size and fury.

A typical summer shower will swell the Storm Devils to several times their normal size. As they grow, they get more aggressive. A knee-high skunk isn't so scary until it charges, hissing and gnashing its teeth. The caw of an eagle-sized crow, talons aimed at your skull, sounds a lot like a human scream.

Your mother told you to have more sense than to play in the rain, and in Florida, at least, she was right.

There is theoretically no limit to how big a Storm Devil can get. When the sky's dark castles collapse over land, sending torrents of wind-driven rain, an ambushed walker with an exploded umbrella may find himself face to face with a bear-sized raccoon, its red eyes wide as brake lights. And such storms are frequent in Florida, especially in summer, when the hot, humid days take umbrage at their own swelter.

As if a hurricane's damage isn't enough by itself, think of the giants stomping around outside while you huddle under a mattress in your shuddering bathtub. Are those tree limbs falling on your roof or the smacks of a giant possum tail? Is that golf ball-sized hail you hear or ostrich-sized woodpeckers jabbing their tremendous beaks through your shingles and down into your attic? And that pounding at the door—is that the buffeting wind or the snout of thirty foot gator?

Hear its hiss between gusts? The door is weakening. So is the frame. Won't be long now.

Still, you might survive, even if your house doesn't. In the aftermath, when rows of manufactured homes look stomped upon and entire neighborhoods' worth of trees look shoved aside, who's to say they haven't been? The swollen Storm Devils have cut a path through your neighborhood just to satisfy their monstrous rage. And when the storm passes and the skies open onto a bright morning sun and the survivors step out and assess the damage, who's to say that raccoon rooting through the splintered remains of your house wasn't the beast who destroyed it in the first place?

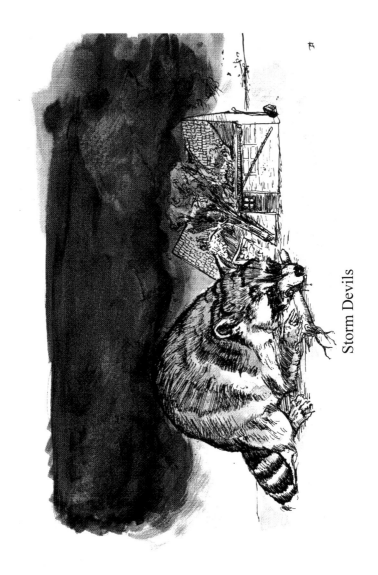

Storm Devils

Okeechobee Flatwhales

By day, Lake Okeechobee is a flat expanse of infinite blue, an inland sea so shallow it seems unexpectedly fragile, like a saucer of milk put out for a giant stray cat. Though it's the second largest body of inland water in the lower 48, its average depth is nine feet and it bottoms out at twenty. Before the Herbert Hoover Dike was constructed, a pair of hurricanes in 1926 and 1928 shoved water out of the lake and flooded the towns and farmlands on the south side, killing 2500 people. While the dike and the system of canals and levees built after it prevented further flooding and opened up the middle of the state for farming and cattle grazing, they also shrank the lake's wetlands and restricted the flow of water into the Everglades, effectively damming the River of Grass.

As is often the case, artificial control solved one natural problem and created a thousand new ones. Damage to submerged plant beds now threatens the fish population. Freshwater discharge into estuaries upsets delicate ecosystems. Invasive exotic plant species crowd out the natives along the shore. Agricultural run-off settles into a layer of phosphorous-rich mud at the bottom. It's from this organic mud that the Okeechobee Flatwhale sucks its meals.

While Big O. fishing guides brag of "monster" bass, they're of course speaking in relative terms—nine pounds if you're lucky. Okeechobee isn't deep enough for true monsters—at least not ones of that shape. A Lake O. monster would have to be flat and wide—a horizontal swimmer, rather than a vertical one—like a giant flounder, which, it so happens, is about the shape of the Flatwhale.

But the fishing guides won't tell you about Flatwhales. You'll have to tune into the whispers of the bar crowd on a slow afternoon in Clewiston or Pahokee or Buckhead Ridge. And then you may not believe it unless you see for yourself.

In that case, rent a boat—if you can find a marina willing to rent you one at night, for night is the time the Flatwhales are reported to come up for air. They take only one breath each day, inhaling a quantity of air that doubles their thickness and leaves them immobile for several hours just below the surface, resting while the carbon dioxide slowly bubbles up from their twin blowholes.

You leave from a marina in Clewiston, let's say, in an old wooden jon boat with a couple of fiberglass chairs bolted to the deck and an 18-horse outboard stuck on the back. You've brought a camera and some infrared binoculars, an army surplus item you paid too much for on eBay. But it will all be worth it if you can snag a photo of the legendary Flatwhale. You'll sell the photo and your story to a grocery check-out rag and pay your rent for a while.

You cut the motor. You're far from shore, the glow of Clewiston barely visible on the horizon. You probably should have brought a GPS. But if worse came to worse, you could spend the night out here in calm waters and find your way back in the morning. No need to panic.

Except now you feel a light breeze and it's gathering strength. There are no clouds, only a high haze that mutes the stars and smears the half moon. You feel a chill. A scan through your infrared binoculars reveals nothing. In fact they don't seem to work worth a damn; either you or the military got ripped off.

As the breeze turns to a strong gale, you notice the boat picking up speed, getting shoved along. The flat bottom smacks the whitecaps, and you find you have to slide off the fiberglass chair and huddle on the deck so you don't get flung overboard.

That's when you notice the boat is taking on water, sloshing against your knees. As you bail uselessly with an empty tall-boy, you also notice something strange about the gale. It's steady. Too steady. There's none of the gusting and swirling you usually get at the front edge of a storm. This is a strong, steady blow from one direction.

Or else a suck from the other.

And now you understand. You abandon the bailing and try the binoculars again, finally toss them into the waves, wondering too late if you'd simply forgotten to take off the lens caps.

The only equipment you have left is your camera. As wind speed approaches hurricane strength, your jon boat rattles across the wave tops. It could flip at any moment. You must be getting close to the source of the vacuum.

Kneeling in the boat, one hand clinging to the leg of a seat, you manage a single flash photo before you lose your grip and get lifted out.

You're flying, you're flailing, and suddenly it's calm.

You seem to be inside something. But you're alive, you think. Are you floating? You're not sure. You feel nothing except the camera still gripped in your hand. You hear now the unmistakable rush of blood and the impossibly slow thunder of a giant beating heart.

All you can do is wait it out. You're drifting weightlessly, as in death, except there's no chorus of angels and no shining overhead light. You remind yourself that if you survive this you'll be famous.

After a while—you have no idea how long—the ceiling of this cavern you're in begins to lower. You've got to crouch tighter and tighter. You wonder if you're going to suffocate. The air's getting stale, and your head's getting squeezed.

And then—pop! —you burst out of the flattening room, reborn in a shallow sea. You bubble up through four feet of water and into the light of dawn. A miracle!

The sky is pale and pink at the edges. The air is still. You're glad to be alive. Thirty yards away, your rented jon boat drifts gently in the rippling lake. You kick over and climb in.

You're saved!

And you've still got your camera!

If the camera's memory card hasn't been destroyed, you might even have your picture.

You're trembling with gratitude and anticipation as you fire up the outboard.

And you're still trembling when you get home and insert the memory card into your computer.

But the picture's not what you hoped for. It's a flash photo of a worried-looking bird you later determine is a snail kite, an endangered raptor that feeds on snails in the declining marshlands around the lake.

No lake monster. Not even a grainy shot of its twin blowholes.

You have a story to sell, but, after some thought, you decide not to go public with it. No one will believe that snail kite was flying backwards, let alone your claim that you spent the night in the lungs of a Flatwhale.

Well, maybe the tabloids would buy it for a reduced fee, enough to cover your rent for a few months. But the bad publicity would cause you a thousand new problems down the road. You've had enough of those.

In a rare exercise of good judgment, you erase the image and go to bed. Some things, you decide, are best kept as they are.

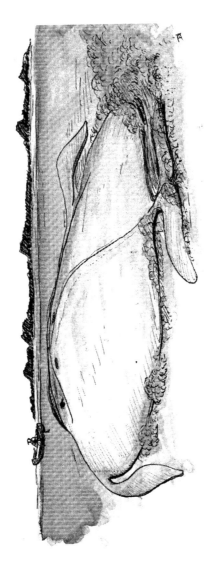

Okeechobee Flatwhales

Peat Fairies

To many, the great mysteries of the past have vanished completely and we live now in a world stripped bare by the cold fingers of science. We no longer allow ourselves the seduction of half-veiled truths. We don't linger on their mystery. Instead, we expect the world to lie still and unclothed beneath our measured gaze, submitting to our insatiable curiosity with a sad, passionless sigh.

Fortunately, there's a law of the universe known as Conservation of Mystery, according to which the amount of mystery in the universe is both finite and unchanging. This means that mysteries may be split into fragments but never destroyed, not completely. Think of mercury drops on a plate.

And because mystery is conserved, "solving" a mystery is actually the act of pulverizing it into seemingly more manageable fragments—or fragments so tiny we hardly detect them at all.

What, then, of all the great mysteries that once held the attention of cavemen, monks, and philosophers? Their remnants are a thin mist now, the dark matter of our everyday lives. It takes effort even to notice them, and if there's any value to this modest book, it's to gather these remnants into your cupped palms, so you may drink them in again.

Here's one.

Throughout the 19th century a plume of smoke and flames rose above the swamps of the Big Bend, the humid armpit of the Florida panhandle. Well-known to locals and visitors and to sailors in the Gulf, the mysterious plume was frequently investigated by expeditions of fortune-seekers.

Both swamp and mystery proved impenetrable.

"The country seems as wild and unexplored as the worst jungles of Africa," one man wrote in the *Florida Dispatch*. In addition to the poisonous snakes, 20-foot alligators, and bloodthirsty insects, the Wakulla Swamp had fortified itself with battlements of sawing, needling, stinging plants; sucking mud-sloughs; rivers that disappeared and reappeared from out of the limestone bed; and huge flint boulders scattered as if by volcanic explosion.

The mystery endured. Some said the plume rose from the campfire of a band of pirates or runaway slaves, or from a coven of witches mixing vats of devilry. Others claimed it had always been there and cited as evidence the Indian derivation of *Wakulla*: "mist," or "mysterious water." The more scientific-minded insisted that a new volcano was emerging from out of the swamps.

Despite numerous setbacks, including malaria, snake bites, and paralyzing fear, teams of investigators inched closer with each new expedition. It seemed only a matter of time.

Then one day the plume vanished for good. It happened on a date near enough to the Great Charleston earthquake of 1886 that the weary, bug-bitten fortune seekers had an out. They claimed the quake had disturbed the earth just enough to douse the source of the plume, like dirt over a campfire.

Mystery solved, they could all go home. It had probably been swamp gas or a slow-burning fire all along.

But a few knew the truth. They were the ones who understood the swamp and saw her thorny plants and venomous reptiles not as hindrances to be slashed and burned on a march to glory, but as an opportunity to flirt, to test the swamp's dark waters when the waters allowed it, to retreat when they did not. These people—mostly former slaves and hermits with shady backgrounds—had lived with the swamp for years and had grown to respect it. Only when the swamp allowed it did they sometimes stumble upon the Peat Fairies, the true source of the mysterious plume.

Now their stories come to us as half-remembered whispers from great-grandparents: *I once knew a man who knew someone else who claimed to see the most amazing thing…*

Smoldering, egg-shaped creatures about the size of small dogs, Peat Fairies have a thick, coarse hide, a smoking mesh of decayed plant material, that seems always about to burst into flames. Their huge teardrop eyes flicker and glow but never blink. From the vent at the top of their pointed heads, a steady stream of smoke curls upward as from a handful of cigarettes.

They congregate around bogs, and there, with their tiny legs and floppy arms, they perform a sort of waddling, ritualized dance with flashing eyes and crackling flesh. As they step and hop on the spongy earth, they peel off layer after layer of gauzy flesh from their thick hide, like Salome with her veils, yet they never seem to reveal anything beneath—not blood, nor organs, nor even a fresh layer of skin.

We don't know why they dance. We don't know what they want. But a viewer lucky enough to see them is mesmerized anyway. It's as if each moment of their dance renews a mystery without ever giving hope of solving it.

They must communicate somehow, for at certain moments their movements synchronize and they all touch their heads together at once. Flames shoot from their cranial chimneys, a huge, fiery plume flashes up through the trees, and their previously hidden mouths open wide and emit an astonished huff-huff before the dance begins again.

But they are no longer seen in the Wakulla Swamp. In the years since the last investigation, the trees of

Wakulla have been cut for timber and the ground's been pierced for oil. The swamp is tame enough now for family vacations, and the legend of the volcano has been explained away or forgotten.

Another mystery solved, and the fanciful explanations about witches and volcanoes seem now only the child-like imaginings of a primitive people.

But what happened to the Peat Fairies, the little dancing mysteries of the Wakulla?

Either someone tipped them off or they themselves saw what was coming, the march of progress tightening its noose. They dispersed like smoke.

Which is not to say they disappeared. The mystery is conserved, as the law of the universe demands, and you can find them still, if you try. As you drive a lonely road in Florida at dusk, you may pass an abandoned trailer tucked down a two-track lane; behind it a small plume of smoke rises up through the trees. If you aren't in such a hurry to get where you're going, you could pull off and turn around. You could step quietly around the back of the burnt-out trailer. And there you'd find yourself seduced by a dance of veils, the Peat Fairies peeling off skin and putting their smoldering heads together, shooting little flames like mysteries into the sky.

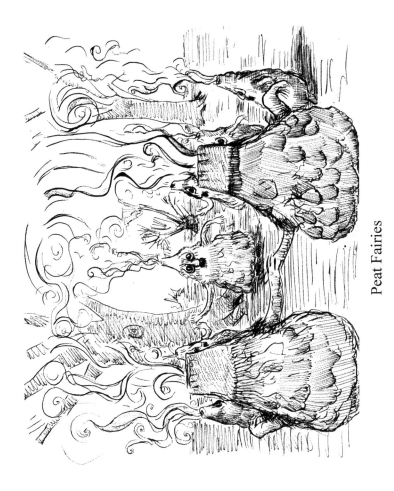

Peat Fairies

Ghost of the Monkeynaut

These are the hard facts: On December 13, 1958, a navy-trained squirrel monkey named Gordo was launched from Cape Canaveral in a Jupiter rocket. Telemetry data—from a microphone taped to his chest—suggest that Gordo survived the launch and his weightless moments in space but died when his parachute failed to open and the rocket's nosecone sank to the bottom of the Atlantic. The U.S. Army abandoned the search for this missing hero after six hours.

Then, in early 1959, reports began surfacing of a small, monkey-like creature wrapped in a foil suit and a sad little plastic helmet haunting the coast. He walked the beach mournfully at night, tail dragging in the sand, whimpers fading in and out with the ocean breeze. If approached, he scampered up a palm tree and disappeared into the night sky. One group of concerned citizens in Satellite Beach seemed to have encircled him until their flashlights all blinked out at once. At least one man felt a cold breeze on his knee and the flick of a furry tail.

What had they seen? Gordo or his ghost? Had Gordo's chutes deployed after all, lowering his little craft into the Gulf Stream, where it bobbed and drifted until it washed ashore on a quiet stretch of beach?

Perhaps it doesn't matter. Life and death is of little concern to a monkey who has stared down the empty depths of the universe and fallen to earth without the consolation of fame—or even so much as a pair of warm arms to run to and hide.

They say that abandoned heroes do not go quietly. Gordo had been trained using little rewards, fruit to pull a lever, nuts to push a button, sweets to lie still for five minutes and breathe slowly. He'd done what they'd asked and been promised so much more than treats, though he'd never wanted it. Now, when he'd given his life to the program, the least they could do was pay respect to his feat.

For several years, Gordo was spotted up and down the Space Coast. Later reports hint at a growing bitterness and desperation. No longer the whimpering, abandoned little monkey, Gordo crept up on late-night lovers and sank his teeth into their sandy calves. He stared fiercely through the sliding doors of first-floor condos and banged insistently on the glass, eyes aglow with the accusatory intelligence of a creature who knows too much.

"He seemed to want my attention," reported one frightened condo owner. "He pounded harder when I looked away."

The last recorded sighting was by a Cocoa Beach motel owner in 1970 who described a tiny old spaceman on the beach at night. Wires that had once connected Gordo to the scientists back home now splayed from his shiny suit, the microphone to record the beats of his tiny heart monitored by no one. He slouched up the beach toward the Saturn V rocket sitting that night on the Cape Canaveral launch pad. One likes to think Gordo stowed away and found a quiet glory in his second and last visit to space. One likes to think he abandoned his bitter quest for attention, fame being small consolation for a monkey who never wished to climb higher than a tree.

Except, there's one more hard fact to his story: the rocket on the launch pad that night was Apollo 13.

Ghost of the Monkeynaut

The St. Vincent Sambar

St. Vincent Island floats off of Florida's Forgotten Coast like a detached moth wing, striations of chenier sand ridges sweeping across it like veins. Isolated, yet a short boat ride from shore, the island seemed perfect for new owners—in 1908 and again in 1948—to establish an exotic game preserve. Zebras, elands, black bucks, and Asian water fowl, among others, were imported at great expense and then hunted in a Florida-style safari between ridges and the oyster-shell middens of prehistoric aborigines.

The zebras, elands, and every exotic but the Sambar vanished from St. Vincent Island long ago. No one knows for certain why. They may have been hunted to extinction, or driven by boredom or homesickness to suicidal leaps into the surf. With limited natural resources, they may have fallen prey to a concentrated and unintended experiment in survival of the fittest. In that case, the Sambar are the victors. They coexist peaceably with the smaller, domestic, white-tailed deer only because they occupy different ecological niches on the island.

A native of Southeast Asia, the Sambar can weigh up to 700 pounds, and it is known among hunters for its cunning, its stags' impressive three-pointed antlers, and the foghorn blast of its alarm bark. Those brave enough to venture out at night from the primitive campsites on St. Vincent risk a heart-stopping jolt from this booming bark—and, some say, a scare far more terrifying yet.

Among the Sambar of St. Vincent Island there are some, it's said, who stalk the human visitors, turning the tables on decades of human predation, particularly on those foolish or careless enough to find themselves alone under the slash pine of the interdune flats or the arthritic fingers of the old live oaks.

There, in darkness, you may find yourself hunted. Pausing on your walk, you may hear a heavy step, and then silence. The thick, trembling breath of an agitated beast, and again silence. You may spy the flash of an antler before the moon slips behind a cloud. It's clear now the beast stands between you and the campsite, waiting.

You may sense its anger, its unease. You may be frightened, and yet not nearly so frightened as after the brief moment of stillness when you find yourself contemplating the nature of the beast's existence, how it was brought here long ago to this subtropical paradise, how for a short time life seemed easy. And then the hunters came, food grew scarce, and survival became no less a struggle than back home. Perhaps more so.

You, too, are an outsider, having been lured to Florida with attractive images of sunsets and easy living and the seduction of a clean break. Later, the house of postcards collapsed, along with both the life you knew and the one you were promised. You felt taken.

So it's not hard for you to imagine life in the Sambar's four hooves (though you know now it is no longer alive in the usual sense). You think how when a roam in any direction brings you to the water's edge, your life starts to feel small and cut off. The other Sambar you once knew have died from the struggle, or from diseases you'd never imagined, and now you are lonelier than you'd ever thought possible, even in the midst of a herd. Seeing your own kind only reminds you of what you've lost.

You're drawn now exclusively to visitors, both angered and fascinated by their newness and ignorance. You want to harm them, to scare them off, but also to reach out to each one as perhaps the very last creature on earth who can tell you what went wrong.

You don't. After all these years, you lack the strength even for that.

Then, when the beast's horn blasts again, waking you out of your depressing ruminations and stopping your heart, you understand, perhaps too late to recover, that this is how it works: in your moment of weakness, the demon deer has invited you into its nightmare. He has made you see it as your own.

The St. Vincent Sambar

The Were-Panther

With fewer than one hundred left in the wild, the Florida Panther ranks high on the state's endangered species list.

The population of its cousin, the Florida Were-Panther, has never exceeded one.

Yet no one is putting the Were-Panther on the endangered list. Certainly not the late-night drivers on Alligator Alley. They're the ones most likely to encounter the Were-Panther; and in that case, they're the endangered ones.

"Alligator Alley," sarcastically labeled by the AAA when it was first planned, links the southwest and southeast coasts of Florida. Originally a two-lane state road, it's been widened and absorbed into the interstate system to serve the needs of the exploding coastal populations. Still, it can be lonely at night, a hundred miles of sawgrass, canals, and toothy beasts, with outposts of civilization few and far between.

Sometimes it has to be driven, though, and you can't always choose your time of day. There are people to meet, deals to make, and business in Miami starts early. So you fill your SUV's tank, dutifully check the oil, belts, headlights, and cell phone battery. You ease behind the wheel and accelerate into the night.

The patches of night fog don't bother you much. You maintain a healthy eighty miles per hour in sparse traffic. Red eyes flicker in the black canals on either side of the road to keep you alert. The engine hums, the A/C fills the cabin with a pocket of cool air, and an iPod broadcasts a random sequence of your favorite tunes. All of it—including the great momentum of your two and a half ton SUV—creates the illusion of invincibility. What could possibly halt the meaningful progress of your vehicle, or the next guitar riff of your third favorite song, or the next beat of your healthy, well-exercised heart?

You yawn. Only forty miles to go.

And it's right about then, in that brief moment of complacency as you lean back in your seat to ease the lumbar strain, as you allow your eyelids a slower-than-average blink, that a puff of dense fog swallows your pocket of invincibility. The Were-Panther pounces, claws wide, eyes aglow, directly through the safety glass of your windshield.

The beast may simply be a mutant Florida panther, the product of generations of inbreeding within a tiny population. For a species dying off from extreme environmental degradation, even a bizarre genetic mutation may prove successful. And who knows what mutations decades of pollution can produce? If the animal cannot easily reproduce itself by normal means it will inevitably seek alternatives.

Some say the Were-Panther is actually a product of the U.S. Fish and Wildlife Service's crossbreeding program, in which another species of panther, the Texas cougar, was brought in to interbreed with the Florida panther. Reports of Were-Cougars in the Southwest date back as far as Indian petroglyphs. One of them may have been brought here by mistake.

Were-Cougars are known to attack pedestrians; the Florida Were-Panther never does. That's why a stalled motorist on Alligator Alley at 2 a.m. is safe—from one creature, at least. For the Were-Panther may only reproduce itself by piercing the flesh of a human traveling at least 75 miles per hour, passing away even as it passes on its mutant genes.

From out of the fog, the Were-Panther strikes. Nuggets of safety glass fly everywhere. The beast's curiously hand-like claws pierce the flesh of the aghast driver who could be you. Snout collides with face, fur with skin, and an unblessed union of species occurs at high speed as the vehicle careens off the road, through the guardrail, into the black mirror of the canal.

Before the gators move in, a new creature emerges from the sinking vehicle, climbs onto the roof with the easy grace of a four-legged predator, and leaps to the grassy bank.

Only one man has survived a Were-Panther attack, and that was only for a short time. The beast lunged through the windshield of his truck, grazed his cheek with one claw, then exited the rear window and ended up dead in his truckbed. The man eased his truck into a Miccosukee Indian-run gas station and burst through the door quaking and bloody. He told his story to the station owner in a trembling voice, returning again and again to the red eyes, so weirdly human and maniacally determined.

When the station owner squinted in disbelief, the man begged him to go check the back of his truck. Sure enough, the glass had been blown out of both the windshield and the rear window of the cab. Fingers of blood crept between ridges of the truck bed like irrigation canals. But no panther or beast of any kind.

When the owner returned to the convenience store, the man, too, was gone. In his place, a few tufts of beige animal hair stuck to droplets of blood on the floor. The case was never solved.

And the Were-Panther lives on. Even with a population of one, it will never be eligible for the endangered species list.

Not as long as there are cars on the Florida highways and complacent drivers behind the wheel.

The Were-Panther

Creatures of the Beach

Even a child knows not to lay a beach towel over a crab's hole. But is that hole really a crab's? And even if a crab does emerge, might it not be because something has scared it from below, and the crab finds you the lesser of two monsters?

To the invading tourists crowding the Florida beaches each year, the sand is a kind of DMZ. The tourists plant their umbrellas and unfurl their bright-colored towels for a few carefree hours beyond the slings and arrows of land-life. If they venture into the water, they don't, in the big scheme of things, stray too far from shore. They've seen the aerial shots, the sharp outlines of 6000-tooth torpedoes prowling through the oblivious bathers. Beachgoers may play in the shore break or cool their feet in the froth, but most of all they lie on the sand and soak up the unobstructed sun, clinging to an illusion of carefree living.

Most have no idea of the dangers lurking directly beneath their cushioned behinds.

Consider the **Atlantic Sand Snake**, a translucent and eyeless 30-foot constrictor. With millions of tiny "breathing pores" all over its body, it can suck oxygen from between grains of sand as it spears its way beneath the beach. Sensitive to vibration, it can "feel" the breath of a solitary sun-worshipper on a lonely stretch of sand, or one who has dozed off and stayed too late on the public beach. Its spade-shaped head, tongueless and sand-coated, shoots up and twists in the breeze until it locates its prey, then falls heavily across the victim's belly and presses him into the sand. It coils itself around the victim's torso and takes him under, where he suffocates by—you name it—the constrictor's tight squeeze, the mouthfuls of sand sucked into his lungs, or the airtight clamp of the creature's gullet. How many times have you spotted a splintered beach chair on an otherwise empty beach and wondered what could have happened? Now you know.

In the mid-80s, a pair of scientists working in secret on the grounds of the former Koreshan Unity Settlement successfully combined the DNA of a Florida sand flea with an Africanized honey ("killer") bee. No one knows why this was done. Inevitably, the experiment escaped, mated with the local sand fleas, and from the eggs hatched a new terror for Southwest Florida beachgoers. These **Killer Sand Fleas** swarm at dusk and dawn, lifting out of the sand with a ravenous appetite for blood. Because they are white or sand-colored, they may be mistaken at first for a patch of fog. That misimpression is quickly corrected when the swarm engulfs you and the bugs pierce your flesh with serrated mandibles and lick up your blood. They get in your mouth and nostrils and bite you from the inside. Your tongue swells; you can no longer yell. If you make it back to your car, they will follow you in through the A/C vents. Somehow they can sense when your body goes into shock, and they always stop short of killing you. No one knows why. Perhaps it is only so they can attack you again.

Like the ant-lion larvae, the **Sand Lion** digs a pit like an inverted cone and devours prey who fall into its trap. But the Sand Lions are much bigger, about the size of hedgehogs, and they work in teams to build their cones directly under creatures who rest too long on the sand. They spin slowly at first, descending deeper and deeper into the beach. The sunbather will sink imperceptibly. If she feels a slight rotational tug, she'll readjust her beach towel and bathing suit straps and close her eyes again. She may feel the brief sense of vertigo you get when you spin off into sleep. And if she opens her eyes, she'll indeed find herself spinning down into the sand. The Sand Lions have drawn her into a sandy whirlpool now, twisting and sucking, and when she reaches the vortex, she'll find there the snapping, saw-like teeth of a pack of Sand Lions tearing her overtanned flesh from her bones.

When they have finished their meal, the Sand Lions carefully restore the beach to its smooth appearance. The next beachgoer who happens along will roll out his towel and lean back on his inflatable pillow, oblivious as always to the horrors below.

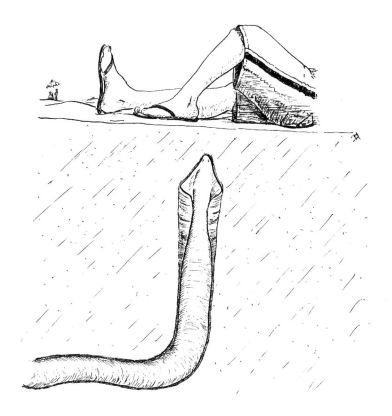

The Atlantic Sand Snake

The Mermaid Vampire of Weeki Wachee Springs

In 1960-1961, a series of unexplained deaths rocked the small towns near Weeki Wachee Springs, an attraction famous for its underwater mermaid shows. The first death might have been dismissed as a simple case of bathtub drowning, except that the victim, a six-foot, fifty-something widower, was found with his head resting on the tub's ledge, a wet rose clenched in his teeth, while a damp trail led out of the bathroom and across the carpet of his trailer to the wide-open front door.

A week later, another man was discovered drowned in his bed, completely naked, sheets and mattress soaked through. When the coroner rolled him over, a gallon of cold water spilled from his blue lips.

More bodies followed, nine in a six month span, some in their beds, some in their tubs. One was found in a row boat on his private pond, a bass still tugging at his fishing line. Another lay on a soaking wet picnic blanket in the shade of a live oak, a basket of cheese and crackers flipped open, a bottle of Bordeaux uncorked and half empty.

The victims had one thing in common beside the cause of death: they were all single men between the ages of 27 and 55.

At the request of public officials—some of them also single men who'd begun locking their doors at night—the sheriff's departments of Hernando and Citrus counties kept details of these deaths secret. It was high season for tourism.

At last in the summer of 1961 came a break in the case: a victim in Spring Hill had clawed off a small filet of his killer's flesh. The sample shimmered under the microscope, a curious amalgam of skin and scales.

Late that night, to avoid notice, the police dogs were given a whiff and set loose. They led a team of investigators directly to the employee entrance of Weeki Wachee Springs.

The detectives began asking questions—of the manager, the staff, and the mermaids. The owners at the time, the American Broadcasting Corporation, grew nervous about their investment and instructed everyone at the attraction to cooperate fully, the manager to fire anyone who looked remotely suspicious.

For every mermaid interviewed, "suspicious" brought to mind a certain employee.

"Well, there *is* one girl, a real oddball and a snoot," they said. "She won't socialize with anyone, won't smile except under water."

Her name was Angela DiMare. She'd arrived the previous year under mysterious circumstances. Even the manager hadn't remembered hiring her. But she could hold her breath longer than the other girls, she had a sharp, unearthly beauty, and, though she rarely rehearsed, her flawless performances as the wicked witch in Snow White and as the crocodile in Peter Pan never failed to impress visitors.

No one knew where she lived, nor had anyone ever seen her outside the attraction. Every time the detectives showed up, she went home sick. One detective dressed as a tourist and came for the show, determined to catch up with her at last. He watched and waited and quickly found himself transfixed by her performance. Her expression held such an unbearable depth of sadness, and her graceful movements were so full of yearning, the detective had to bury his face in his hands and weep. He'd never expected to fall in love with a witch.

He bought a carnation and waited for her outside the tube the performers used to get in and out of the spring. She never appeared.

Had she slipped into the Weeki Wachee River and climbed out downstream? Had she descended deep into the unexplored caverns of the springs?

About this time, Elvis Presley was in the area filming *Follow That Dream* up in Yankeetown and other locations along the coast. The excitement generated by Elvis kept the attention off what the police now referred to as the Mermaid Vampire.

On July 30, 1961, Elvis paid a visit to Weeki Wachee, and 15,000 fans turned up to see him. He watched the show, then joked with reporters and signed autographs for fans. He posed with his arms around the mermaids, two or three at a time. One surviving picture shows Elvis with his arm around the still-wet shoulder of a single, beautiful, fierce-eyed young mermaid. She stares at the camera with an enigmatic smile, glowing cheekbones, and a poise that outshines even the King's allure. Just after the photo was taken, she turned to Elvis as if expecting an invitation. Instead, his handlers pulled him to a new group of autograph seekers and a photo op with ABC execs.

What would have happened if Elvis had paused just a moment longer to look into those eyes?

"Are you lonesome tonight?" jokes the King.

And her eyes say yes. He slips her a key even as he's pulled back into the crowd.

Later, when she lets herself into his hotel room, he's already in bed in his silk boxers. He leans up on one elbow.

"Priscilla warned me not to go chasing tail," he jokes.

She glides to him across the room.

"Honey darling, the manager's going to charge me extra to dry out that wet carpet."

She slides into bed and wraps her arms around him, runs her fingers through his hair. She presses her lips to his, stares deep into his eyes, and nearly devours him with desire.

"I ain't never been kissed by a mermaid," he says and pulls her closer, fumbling for the seam of her costume tail. He never finds it. Instead, her moist lips cover his, and Elvis shudders as if he's never known passion before. The heaviness in his lungs rises into his throat, his mouth. He opens his eyes, startled, but his desire is so strong he can't pull away, not even to breathe. *When we kiss my heart's on fire / Burning with strange desire.* And there's nothing left for Elvis but to surrender.

> *Your lips, your arms, your heart, dear*
> *Be mine forever*
> *Be mine tonight*

This is how it ends for the King, in a hotel bungalow in Crystal River. No more bad movies to be made. No tragic fade to his fortunes or his health. Only a moment of passion that beat anything he'd ever sung about.

Every so often, Weeki Wachee holds a reunion for its mermaids, and they come and pose for pictures. Some of them, even those in their 60s and 70s, keep in good shape. They dive into the spring and give a performance almost as sharp as forty years before.

If you turn your head and look deep into the spring, you may spot her, slipping from out of a cave, still-youthful and fierce, her smile more wistful now, as she remembers the time she nearly drowned the King and became his Queen forever.

The Mermaid Vampire of Weeki Wachee Springs

Links Sprites

It's a joke you tell around the clubhouse after you lost three balls in the woods: "the Links Sprites were busy today." You shot an 89, embarrassing yourself in front of better golfers.

"You're a lucky man," says another guy in your foursome. He nods gravely and strokes his beard. You don't know him well. He's an acquaintance of an acquaintance, a last-minute replacement for a friend with the flu, and he's got a thick, graying beard and a funny accent. He speaks rarely but with such gravity you're inclined to take him seriously. But what can you say? You don't feel lucky; you feel like a schmuck. You take a big swig of your scotch and ask for another.

What the man knows but doesn't say is that Links Sprites, the mischievous little creatures from beyond the white stakes, the ones who are said to steal golf balls or throw them twenty yards away, are capable of far worse, particularly after they've already tricked you twice in one day. As the saying goes, fool me once shame on you, fool me twice shame on me. And the third time? You don't want to know. But I'll tell you anyway.

Links Sprites make their homes in the tall grasses and bushes in the out-of-bounds of golf courses. Some say they're invisible to the naked eye. Others say they're simply too quick to be seen. A few golfers claim to have spotted them; they say the Links Sprites run on two legs, like little men, except they have furry faces with just a hint of a snout to accommodate a sharp set of chompers, and they camouflage themselves with leaves and pine needles stuck to their fur with gooey gobs of spit.

They can strike any time but prefer foggy mornings and dusk. They'll hear the unmistakable thump of a ball sliced into the woods, and they'll dash out of the long grass to grab it with their teeth or their small hairy hands. By the time the golfer eases his golf cart into the woods, a disgusted look on his face, the ball is long gone. He'll put on the parking brake and get out for a look. He's sure he'd seen it land, not too far off the fairway and right between these two pines. Where could it have gone?

There aren't even any shrubs to hide it. He'd been so sure it was right here he hadn't even bothered to hit a provisional ball. Now, with a foursome waiting on the tee, he'll have to take a drop in the rough.

On his backswing, something snickers from deep in the woods.

Must be a squirrel.

After a double bogey, he's determined to steady his game. But the same thing happens on the next hole, and this time the golfer is furious. He makes both his own foursome and the foursome on the tee wait while he searches. Nothing there. He smacks the head of his 6-iron against the bark of the nearest slash pine and sends little blank papyruses flipping end over end to the dirt.

Another drop. Another penalty stroke.

He ignores the little laughing noise in the tall grass. Must be a frog or cicada.

Two holes later, he's so wary of slicing he hooks it instead, sailing the ball across the wide rough and into a stretch of woods rarely in play. Beyond the woods is a marsh, out of bounds.

Disgusted, he tells the rest of his foursome to go on ahead. He'll catch up to them in the clubhouse.

So begins his adventure, bag over his shoulder like a quiver of arrows, club in his hand like a sword. He kicks at mushrooms and jabs at clumps of saw palmetto. Nothing.

Our hero forges ahead, off the course, into the tall grass of the marsh, ignoring the insect bites and the welts on his forearms from the slaps of tall grass.

It's oddly quiet. It makes him wonder, somewhat guiltily, about the natural beauty that must have existed here before the golf course smothered it with a bright green carpet.

An anhinga sticks its snake-neck out of the nearby water like a tiny Loch Ness monster. The wind blows patterns in the marsh grass. A little horse-like whinny escapes the grass nearby. Followed by quick little steps.

His quest is hopeless, he decides. Even if he burned all this marsh grass, he'd never find his ball.

As he turns back to the course, he feels a slight tug on his golf slacks, down around his shin, and before he understands what's happening, a pair of tiny hands grabs his ankle and yanks him down.

Back on the course, his shout goes unheard. His friends are already in the clubhouse nursing their drinks. They'll wait two more drinks before they give up and go home.

No one will see the pattern his body makes in the tall grass as it's dragged off into the marsh. No one will hear his gurgled last gasps.

Fortunately, you, sitting at the clubhouse bar after your poor round of golf, know nothing of this. You've only heard the Links Sprites used as a jokey excuse for a lost ball. You had no idea that the third lost ball put you in great danger, that it was only your willingness to give up so easily that saved your life.

But, after a couple more scotches and a little bit of sulking, you're suddenly offended by the bearded man's comment. What did he mean, "You're a lucky man"? Was he making a sarcastic comment on your game?

You swivel in his direction, ready to demand a clarification, ready to say something that begins with "I'll have you know" and ends with "you son of a bitch," but the man is gone. You could have sworn he was just beyond your elbow at the bar, pulling on his beard, mulling over his own game, listening in on the boasting and the off-color jokes of a Saturday afternoon at the club. He simply vanished.

Well, one more drink and maybe you'll stop caring about that, too. If you're going to keep playing golf, there are some things it's better not to know.

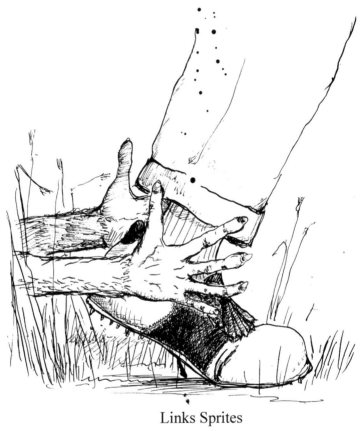

Links Sprites

Key Deer

As you drive south on U.S. 1, the Florida Keys lure you out to sea like a long game of hopscotch, and you willingly skip across the pale blue. When at last you've dead-ended at Key West, you're probably too tired to turn around and hop back to square one. Besides, there are plenty of distractions to occupy a weary traveler for a night or a weekend, distractions that keep you from thinking too much—about, say, how far out to sea you are or how tenuous your connection to the mainland.

The only highway could wash out. A bridge could collapse. The airport could shut down. And then, with a cat five hurricane swirling up out of the Caribbean, you'll be stranded on a slip of lowland destined to vanish under the waves.

If you pause too long between drinks, you'll find yourself searching above the rooftops on Duval Street for a sturdy coconut palm you can cling to in the 180-mph winds.

It's a frequent sight during hurricane season: a ribbon of bumper-to-bumper traffic trying to bolt out of the Keys before a threatening hurricane sandblasts them into the sea. The evacuation can take up to 24 hours, and drivers from the southern keys can expect to spend all day in dense traffic, lurching and braking and pounding their fists on the wheel.

Not surprisingly, some stay home or in their hotels and stock up on liquor instead. Maybe the storm will lose strength. Maybe it will veer away. When it doesn't, some have regrets and try to dash out too late. Yet even if the bridges are still standing and the overwash not too deep on U.S. 1, they may find their way blocked by a steely-eyed gang of Key Deer.

Some call them Conch Republic Border Guards. It's believed the deer arrived in the keys by land bridge during the last ice age. When the ice receded and the seas rose, they got stranded like unlucky tourists and became easy game for Native Americans and European explorers. Later, when the highway was built, they were roadkill for vacationers in rented convertibles and sportsmen hauling oversized fishing boats. Though hunting Key Deer was banned in 1939, poaching and habitat destruction brought them to near extinction.

Somehow, they've survived. The establishment of the National Key Deer Refuge in 1957 helped. Then, too, they must also have developed—perhaps by natural selection—a fierce will to live, a surprising strength that belies their fragile looks. They have a meanness that shows itself only in hurricanes, much like Florida Storm Devils, of which they may even be a subspecies.

There are reports of Key Deer blockades as far back as the Labor Day Hurricane of 1935. In that storm, still the strongest on record to hit the U.S., a train was sent down from Homestead to evacuate a group of World War I veterans building a bridge for the new highway. The train never made it, and some say it was turned back by a gathering of Key Deer. Something, in any case, shoved the train off the track and into the waves.

More recently, a group of Key West residents trying to escape the storm surge from Hurricane Georges in 1998 reportedly were turned back at Big Pine Key, home of the Key Deer Refuge. None of them want to talk about it.

Perhaps all those years at the mercy of humans have put a chip on the Key Deer's tiny shoulders: If I'm not getting out, neither are you.

And so they gather in the storm on a high patch of U.S. 1, and you won't see them unless you're one of the foolish and scared, trying to escape while the storm's underway. You may think you're making good

56

progress out of Key West—your big Caddy seems too heavy to be flipped and its wheels are sticking to the road. And then, at Big Pine, you discover, through the chaotic sweep of your wipers, that your path to safety is blocked by a white-tailed barricade.

Your car slides to a stop some ten feet in front of the herd. Between the roaring torrents and full-throated gusts you catch only glimpses. There must be two hundred of them. In their snarling lips and fierce eyes, you detect an almost supernatural strength of will, a collective determination that only a tribe of survivors can know. They've been hunted and slaughtered and crushed and starved, and still they live.

You try honking the horn but can't even hear it yourself.

If you got out, these creatures would barely come up to your waist. They're cute little pygmies with soft fur and spindly legs. How can they even stand up to the wind? The answer must lie in a group dynamic, the way penguins keep themselves warm by huddling together in the Antarctic winter. The Key Deer are hunkered down. They're not going to move, and they're not going to let you pass.

But there's a strengthening hurricane taking aim at the lower keys; your only hope is to push on.

What can you do? You gun the engine. You let the Caddy lunge at them to scare them off. Nothing doing. You've got an older model Caddy with a big chrome bumper you've jokingly referred to as a cowcatcher. Now you think you'll put it to use.

Except the deer, collectively, have surprising strength. And they're so cute you hate to destroy them. After one halting attempt, you reconsider. Smashing the deer would be like running over a child's favorite pony.

But you have to. You know this. It's either you or the deer.

You press the accelerator. The rear wheels spin but you go nowhere. You've waited too long. The deer have swarmed your vehicle, closing ranks, and some have lifted your bumper. When others get up on their hind legs and peer through your windows, they block the wind and rain, and there's an eerie calm. Their lips sneer and foam, and their huge black eyes are as still as a hurricane's.

Your car lurches. In a panic, you gun the engine, but with your wheels off the ground, the churning motor seems only to add fury to the deer's determination. Slowly, you're carried off the narrow strip of road and the car is spun ninety degrees to give you a view of the pounding waves through your windshield, the rivers of froth flying at you, the relentless force of the storm. You suck in your breath and feel your heart pounding in your chest.

What will you do when your Caddy is dumped into the sea? When you can't open your door against the waves? When the seawater pours in? What will you do when the last bubble of air disappears from the underside of your convertible top? Can you hold your breath? For how long?

In the big scheme of things, your will to live is nothing compared to the Key Deer's. They're going to live; you won't.

And maybe that's their point.

Key Deer

Creatures of the Sinkholes

To most, the topography of Florida seems about as varied as a deflated life raft on a calm sea, interesting only when you get too near the edge or when a hole opens in the middle. And holes do open in Florida; when they open under roads, they suck down asphalt and cars and their unlucky drivers. When they open under houses, they suck down furniture and beds and the people asleep on top of them. Sometimes they open under lakes, as at Lake Jackson in 1999, when the lake water and everything in it—fish, waterfowl, gators— drained out and disappeared.

Where do they all go?

There are millions of years of dead sea creatures to thank for Florida's bedrock. Formerly a marine shelf, the peninsula bulged as the oceans dipped. And then, once the land was exposed, the rains got to work, fingering through the permeable limestone, carving caverns and caves and subsurface aquifers, as well as sinkholes, springs, and disappearing streams. Who knows for sure what fearsome creatures adapted to life in the black tunnels and galleries under our feet?

Here are a few examples, gathered from eyewitness reports over the years.

Sinkhole Worms. Many witnesses have reported tangles of anaconda-sized worms writhing in the frothy gray soup of sinkholes. When these creatures unhinge their jaws and open their mouths the slurping deafens and the suction draws a gale. One slip, and no amount of desperate clawing will keep you from falling in. Your screams will not escape the sound horizon of the worms' powerful vacuum. You'll go quietly into the maw and not be heard from again.

Earth Whales. So-called because they spout geysers of muddy liquid, the Earth Whales actually have little in common with the gentle giants of the sea. Eyeless, and with a mouth at the very tip of its cigar-shaped, scaly body, the creature seems to have no top or bottom. Beneath the earth, their geysers work more like drills, boring through the bedrock to clear a tunnel between aquifers. To melt away limestone, the liquid they spout is highly acidic, causing severe burns on those who wander too close for a snapshot of a rare "Florida geyser."

Balloon Weed. In many cases, Balloon Weed may be the cause of sinkhole formation. Balloon Weeds form in the aquifer and roll themselves into viny balls of muddy vegetation. As the balls expand, they create their own small ecosystem with bugs and worms living at their liquid core. Sometimes, though, during droughts, a Balloon Weed gets trapped in a dried-up cavern, and the complex method of replenishing its liquid core breaks down. The life inside it slowly dies and decomposes, and the gases released press the airtight ball outward. And then the Balloon Weed itself begins dying from the inside out, its own decom-position swelling it like a dying star. A Balloon Weed in this condition may reach thirty feet across before it explodes, shooting dirt and rotting vegetable matter high into the air and leaving an exposed dry crater. The crater may be tempting to explore until you understand that the Balloon Weed, released from its stressed ecosystem, quickly begins to recover, rolling itself into a moist tiny ball, just large enough to wrap around your foot, and then, as it grows, to wrap up your legs, until finally, since your body's 75% water, you find yourself at the core of a new ecosystem slowly draining you of fluids in the darkness.

There's no reason to think that the variety of life under the earth is any less than that above it. I'll leave it to the reader to discover the many other fearsome creatures that certainly lie below us.

Descend, bold traveler!

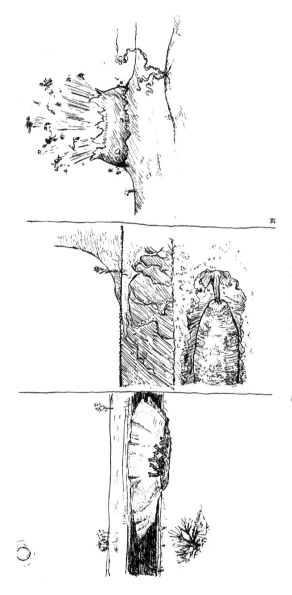

Creatures of the Sinkholes

El Chupacabra

Hey, Chupacabra, you goat-sucking intruder, where
did you come from? No one invited you. No one
opened the door. You dog-paddled across the Florida
Straits. You stowed away in a freighter's hold. You
dug a hole under the fence and squeezed your ugly dog-
snout through, giving the rest of us a bad name. And
then, like us, you were free.

But for what, Chupa? To sleep by day and live in
the dark? To leap from the bush with your kangaroo
legs and ruin our livestock and pets? With two
puncture holes you leave your mark, Chupa. Two tidy
wounds like sacred tattoos, and a clump of dog-hair like
a burning bush. Your religion scares us like a terror
from back home.

Sometimes you take the eyes and leave their dry
sockets gaping to the sky. If a goat like that lives, he
sees only what's past. He's got to guess at what's in
front.

No one asked you to haunt us, Chupa. No one
asked for your sulfur breath in our noses. No one asked
for your face pressed against our bedroom windows,
your cochineal eyes aglow in the dark and the
chalkboard scrape of fangs over glass. We could have
left the blinds open and enjoyed the sight of the moon if
it weren't for you. We could have been at peace.

Instead, we are afraid, though you do not attack us.
We lay our heads on pillows that hold us like soft
serving trays and lift our chins to the night, and still you
leave our bared necks alone. Why do you torture us so?

You settle for the harmless beasts of the field and
we curse you for it. Is that what it's come to for you?
Is that how sad your life? Chupa, you are a sucker in
every sense of the word!

64

But we know it's not true. On still nights, while your bony spikes rattle like bamboo chimes, you stalk your prey and leave us alone, and our angry thoughts do not console us. We are afraid because you do not attack us.

In the morning, we walk through our fields and collect our dead goats, those decomposing mounds of sightless visionaries. How light they are, how airy.

Sometimes, in the heat of the day, we envy their sacrifice. It seems so much worse to know the life you've built could be taken away.

El Chupacabra

The Hanging Trees

Perhaps you're not a beach person. Or perhaps it's summer and the sun's peak strength is enough to stew your already leathery skin like an old boot. Skip the beach, then. Spend time instead in the shade of one of Florida's many picture-perfect oaks. Find one with a bench swing hanging from one of its sturdy limbs. It's a different world there in the shade, older and slower-paced. You're snug and protected in a pocket of calm twilight, shielded from the sun and the rush of days.

Go ahead and put your feet up on the bench. Relax. Rest your head against the chains of the swing and close your weary eyes.

Imagine the history of the huge tree behind and above you, how it predates the Civil War and Florida statehood, perhaps even the birth of the nation. Think of all it's witnessed.

If only you could live that long. How wise you'd be. How rich your life.

As you get more comfortable, the swing seems to dissolve beneath you, and it's as if you're riding on air. You sway a little in the breeze, adrift and weightless. The heat and humidity fade, and the sun is a miniscule speck on the backs of your eyelids.

An odd sensation on your neck disturbs you, a slight tingle at first. The tingle becomes an itch and the itch becomes a burn. Then something tightens around your throat. A slight tug that doesn't release, and when you swallow against it reflexively, it squeezes your neck in response.

What's happening? You want to dismiss it. You're under a tree in a peaceful place. Let's not get carried away and give in to unfounded fears.

You resolve to keep your eyes closed and reason your way out of this uncomfortable feeling. It's imaginary. It's nothing.

But there it is, the rope burn, the tightening. Your eyes are bulging in their sockets. You can barely breathe.

It occurs to you, too late, that you've stumbled into the grip of an old Hanging Tree. The bench swing was only an enticement. Perhaps it was never there at all.

How unlucky can you be? Of all the beautiful old oaks in Florida, why did you have to choose one of the few with an ugly past? This isn't the Deep South, after all.

Perhaps you didn't realize that between 1882 and 1930 Florida had by far the highest per capita black lynching rate in the nation—50% higher than Mississippi's. You didn't know that in 1939 Imperial Wizard James A. Colescot testified before Congress that Florida was the KKK's best stronghold. You didn't know that Fuller Warren, Florida's governor from 1949-1953 had once been a klansman himself. That at least into the 1950s, klansmen held city and county posts throughout Florida, or that in 1951 they engaged in a bombing campaign dubbed "The Florida Terror" to strike fear in would-be black voters. Among those murdered was civil rights leader Harry T. Moore.

Maybe you didn't know any of that; you wandered under the hanging tree as an innocent lover of shade and relaxation.

Too bad, because now the hanging tree is going to fill you in on what you missed.

As the grip tightens around your throat, your gag reflex kicks in. Your tongue reaches out, your chin reaches up. Your legs start to spasm.

How could this be? Why you, of all peace-loving people?

There's a rough, twangy answer in your ear:
Because you let your eyes stray to the wrong woman's chest. Because you argued with someone you shouldn't. Because you were loud in the wrong place. Because you swore too close to church, to our church. Because you stirred up trouble and insulted us. You testified against us. You practiced some sort of voodoo. You stole something. You didn't know your place and dressed above your station. You demanded respect. You tried to vote. You voted for the wrong man.

None of it makes sense. You want to deny everything, but you've got no breath left to make even a sound. Your face is swelling up. Your limbs are going numb. What's going to happen to you?

And the voice responds, reading your thoughts.
When you're done kicking at air, we're going to slice off your toes and sell them as souvenirs. We're going to take your picture and put it on a postcard. We're going to send one to your family and to everyone you knew. And then we'll leave you here to rot, twisting in the wind and defiling this tree like an overripe fruit.

You're losing consciousness now. You make one last attempt to reason your way back to the life you knew, the peaceful person who kept to himself, the mostly good person who deserved a few minutes of rest on a bench swing under an oak.

Was the swing ever there? Were there ever chains that held it to the tree? Was the tree ever real?

But really, the only question that counts is this: Will you ever open your eyes and see for yourself?

The Hanging Trees

Gilda, the Elephant Who Makes Boys Disappear

On a cold day in January 1979, a circus train for the now defunct Zabriskie-Laforge Big Ring Circus derailed in a rural area just outside of Lakeland. Among those killed: a ringmaster's understudy, two cooks, four members of the tent crew, a soccer-playing Arabian stallion, a boxing black bear, two chimpanzee clowns (mother and child), and an elderly Bengal tiger on his way to an exotic animal retirement zoo in Polk County.

Chaos followed. Circus workers—some of them badly injured—struggled to round up spooked zebras, panicky chimps, and the chillingly callous lions watching with steady eyes. Packing the animals together onto the least-damaged cars resulted in bites and maulings and the death of two more horses.

Three boys witnessed the scene from behind a clump of palmetto. What they saw next was so surprising that the boys, usually fearless and loud, could only stare in shocked silence. From out of a toppled train car rolled a full-grown elephant who struggled to her feet, balanced part of the car's roof on her back as if to camouflage herself, and huffed off into the woods.

The boys looked at each other, then at the confusion of the screaming circus workers. No one else seemed to notice.

When the dust settled and the train and its ruined parts were hauled away, the boys were reluctant to tell their story. They feared they'd been the cause of the accident, having put pennies on the track to make copper pancakes. Only after investigators from the NTSB discovered a shattered wheel two miles up the track were they willing to speak.

But who would listen? Not their parents or their teachers. Not the county sheriff or the NTSB. Their claim was ridiculous; no one loses an elephant. Besides, Zabriskie-Laforge Entertainment denied having any elephants on the train. Their only elephant, a 13-year-old Indian female named Gilda, had twice broken her chains and charged the audience in recent months; they claimed she'd been shipped to a small zoo in Indiana.

Except no one bothered to check out Indiana. And no one bothered to check the Zabriskie-Laforge financials. A lost elephant would mean fines and a massive search-and-capture operation, and Zabriskie-Laforge was on the verge of bankruptcy. The circus regrouped for one final sympathy show in Tampa, attended by record crowds. The injured animals performed with limps and winces and half-healed wounds, and the audience gave them standing ovations. Then Zabriskie-Laforge quickly sold off its show animals and equipment, including the few remaining undamaged train cars, and ducked out on creditors. Upper management left the country.

The three boys, determined now to prove their story, met every day after school. They organized "elephant hunts," enlisting the help of their fourth-grade classmates—the ones who didn't laugh at them, anyway. They spread out into the slash pines near the crash site and communicated by walkie-talkie. They scanned the horizon with cheap binoculars. With each false alarm, wasp sting, and poison ivy rash, their enthusiasm flagged.

How long before doubt undermines the fragile architecture of the imagination? For some, not long at all. After six weeks and no trace of an elephant, even the most loyal of their classmates began to make fun of the three witnesses. Then, worst of all, one of the witnesses quit believing he'd seen the elephant in the first place. Another had his doubts.

In the years to come, the boys grew apart. They spoke about the elephant to no one—especially not to each other. Still, the third boy wouldn't let it go. Quietly, in libraries and newspaper archives, he researched the elephant he was sure he'd seen. He tried to ward off doubts with photos from the microfiche. Finally, he scrolled through an old Wisconsin newspaper until he was sure he'd found her, projected right before his eyes as if from a dream.

He compared her with photos of other Indian elephants. Though he'd seen her only for a few seconds and from fifty yards away, he thought he recognized the graceful curve of her forehead, the delicate tail with the frayed-rope end, those soft flaps of ears brushing her jowls, and the rolls of flesh flexing at the knees. Yes, that was Gilda he'd seen. It had to be.

And then, from papers and police reports, he learned of other marks the pictures didn't show. The welts from the whippings. The burns from the cattle prods. The puncture wounds from the bullhooks. This was how they'd trained her, and in between training sessions, they'd kept her in a cage so tight she could not even turn away from her tormentors.

She fought back. In one incident, she threw off a sequined trapeze artist and charged the crowd. In another, she knelt down, dumped a box of children off her back, and crashed through a set of barricades. She took three bullets to the shoulder before they corralled her into a cage.

Is it any wonder that, three weeks later, she rocked the train and shifted her weight and put a strain on the wheels until one broke off? Is it any wonder she survived the wreck, or that she had the wherewithal to camouflage herself and sneak off into the woods when her tormentors were busy saving themselves and their unhappy chattel?

The boy's quiet obsession had already cost him his best friends and his good grades at school. "I hope you'll grow out of it," said his father, shaking his head.

The boy hoped he never would. Gilda hadn't given up, so neither would he.

When he was old enough to drive, he took his elephant hunt on the road in a beat-up Toyota, driving south along State Road 37 through Pierce and Bradley and over to Fort Lonesome. From time to time, he parked on the shoulder and wandered into the woods, seeking a pattern of broken saplings or tall grass yanked up by the roots. He poked and prodded at dung-shaped mounds and sniffed for elephant urine. Sometimes he thought he was onto something; he could never be sure. He'd speak into his old walkie talkie, hoping for a response, a little confirmation from one of his former friends who might have rejoined the search. From anyone who might be listening.

The uncertainty tormented him. How easy it would be to give up and deny he'd seen Gilda in the first place. How easy to live like the others, already getting jobs and getting married and having kids. For them, the derailed circus train was a curious event from childhood, their belief in a runaway elephant something they'd long since outgrown.

Not for him. He'd failed his senior year in high school but took his GED to be done with it. He lived at home and worked as a farm laborer, earning just enough to afford the gas for his investigations. Then, just before his twentieth birthday, he left the house one Sunday morning with a walkie-talkie and a bag of chips and was never seen again.

Some say Gilda, if she really exists, is a kind of monster who operates just this way, drawing boys away

74

from home and out on an endless search through the Neverland of back-country Florida.

Others scoff; some kids just don't grow up, and that's especially true of boys these days.

A few still hear him, though. If you drive through Polk or Hardee county with a walkie-talkie pointed out your window, you might catch a word or two, a report from the field. You might understand what he's after. You might even respond.

And the boy will answer you with a question. He's got a lot of ground to cover and many fearsome creatures to confront, and what he really wants to know is, Are you with him?

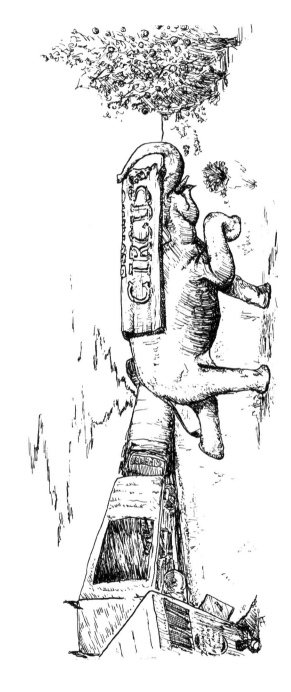

Gilda, the Elephant Who Makes Boys Disappear

CONCLUSION

Some will jeer. Some will yawn.

Some will say I've written this just to scare people away, in the manner of a Scooby-Doo villain throwing his voice and projecting a frightful light show onto wavering billows of homemade fog, or else donning a hairy costume and rampaging through an amusement park, his claim to its ownership hung up in probate court.

Some will say I'm a purveyor of unpleasant fantasies, that I've let an overactive imagination cloud my reason, and that even if these fearsome creatures have been sighted or sniffed or heard as I claim, there are other, more rational explanations for the phenomena than what I've set forth here.

Let them say it.

Let them get comfortable with a cold cocktail on their caged patio beside their shimmering turquoise pool. Let them put their feet up after a warm day on the links and close their eyes, secure in the belief that all life is rational, even in Florida, and that their own rational life has led them step by step to these sublime comforts they experience now: a double vodka tonic and a view across the pool and out to the golf course so picture-postcard-perfect they can shut their eyes to it and see the same thing on the backs of their lids.

All the scene lacks is a "Greetings from Florida" banner.

But perhaps that drink will get too cold in their hand, or perhaps they'll relax so completely it will slip from their fingers and shatter on the flagstone deck.

A small annoyance that snaps the eyes open, and for one instant the postcard overlay jerks slightly out of position like a migrating contact lens, and before it settles, a shadowy figure darts at the edge of vision.

There's a quick shock of recognition, a confirmation of something once read and quickly forgotten.

A fearsome creature?

Maybe. Maybe not. It's already gone.

But there are others, and who's to say you won't be the one to find them.

They may be under your feet, or behind your back, or hanging over your head at this very moment.

They may even be in your house, though that's a subject for another book.

At least now you have a sample of what awaits you when you step off the plane, roll off your hammock, or debark from your luxury cruise ship. The world is less tame than you'd imagined. And if the lighting is right, the air still, and your senses on high alert, you may be lucky enough to see for yourself.

You may even believe it.

ABOUT THE AUTHOR

John Henry Fleming is also the author of *The Legend of the Barefoot Mailman*, a Florida novel. His short stories have appeared in many literary journals, including *McSweeney's, The North American Review, Mississippi Review,* and *Fourteen Hills.* He grew up in Atlantis, Florida, and lived in seven other states before returning in 2001 to teach creative writing at the University of South Florida in Tampa. He lives in Temple Terrace with his wife and children and plays tournament disc golf in his spare time.

ABOUT THE ILLUSTRATOR

A native of South Florida, David Hazouri received his B.A. in English from Duke University, studied painting and drawing at The School of the Art Institute of Chicago, and graduated from University of Miami School of Law. He lives in Miami with his wife and two children, playing competitive tennis, practicing law, and operating his own computer forensics company. He is still looking for our pal Foot-Foot.